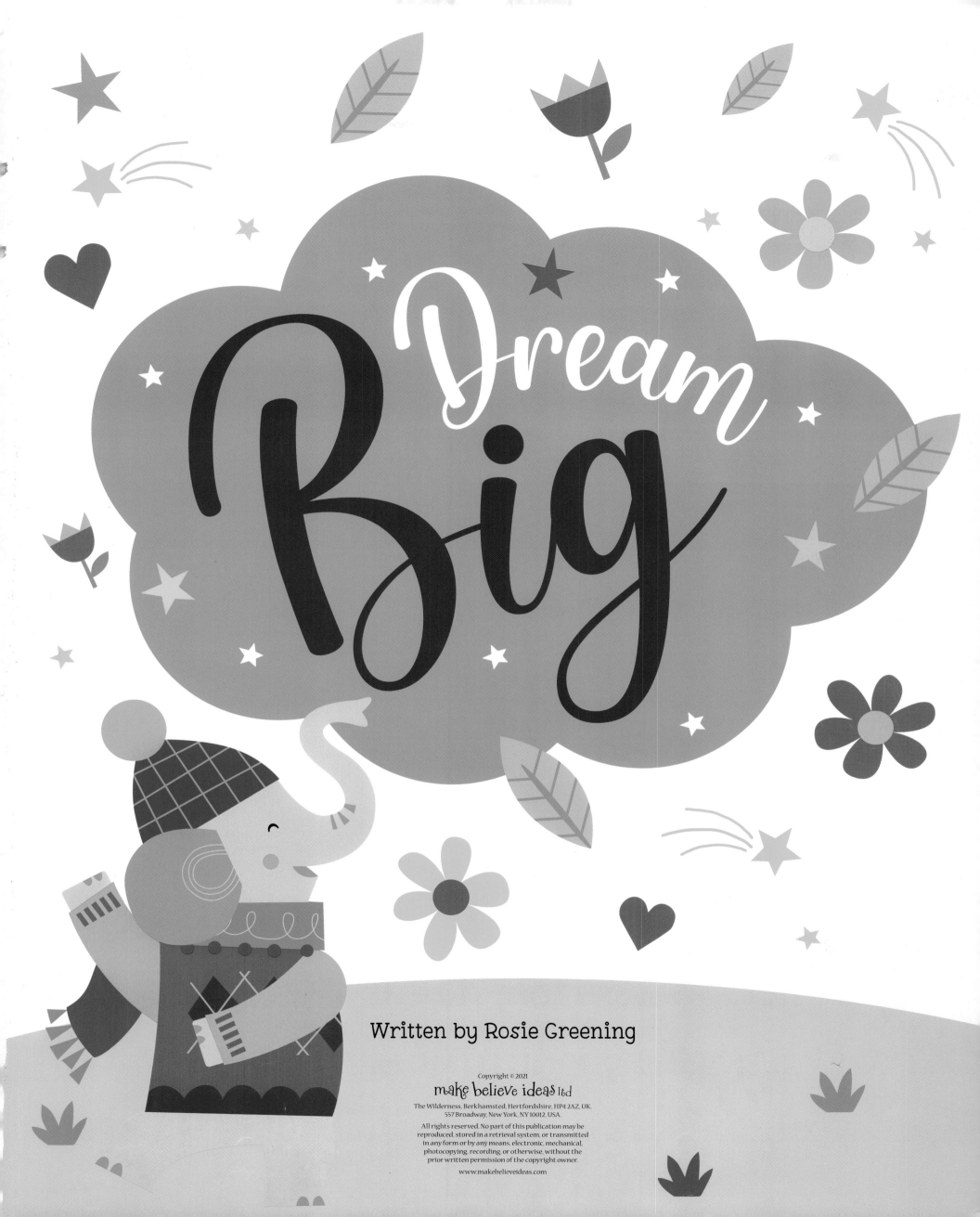

# Dream Big

Written by Rosie Greening

Copyright © 2021
make believe ideas ltd
The Wilderness, Berkhamsted, Hertfordshire, HP4 2AZ, UK.
557 Broadway, New York, NY 10012, USA.

www.makebelieveideas.com

The streets in *Ava's* neighborhood were **gloomy,** dull, and gray.

But no one seemed to notice . . .

until *Ava* did one day.

"Everything needs cheering up,"

thought Ava with a sigh.

"Why won't people stop and look,

instead of rushing by?"

Back home, Ava stared **outside** and **thought** of what she'd seen. She said, "**I wish** I knew a way to make things *bright* and *clean*."

Then she gazed up at the clouds of every shape and size.

"That looks like my elephant!" thought Ava in surprise.

All at once, a voice **boomed** out:

"There's *nothing* you can't do.

You have **everything** you need

to make your *dreams* come true."

"Elephant!"

cried Ava.

"Are you talking to me?"

He said,
"The sky's the limit:
you decide what you can be."

Ava said, "I have a dream, but **where** do I **begin?** I don't think I can **change things** if no one else joins in."

AN A-Z OF AWESOME ACTS

HEROES FROM THE PAST

AMAZING ADVENTURERS

*The Little Book of Big Dreamers*

TIME TO EXPLORE!

DARE TO BE DIFFERENT!

*People Who Changed the World*

Elephant said,

"You can **find**

the **answers** if you **look**."

Then, **suddenly**,

the **sunlight** fell on

**Ava's** shelf of **books**.

Ava started reading and, all at once, she knew these **characters** had changed things, just like she **wanted** to.

TIME TO MAKE A CHANGE

MY GREATEST DISCOVERY

THE JOURNEY OF A LIFETIME

The **people** in the stories
were *kind* and *brave* and *strong.*
Ava felt **inspired** by them,
but **something** still felt **wrong.**

REACH FOR THE STARS

CREATIVITY TAKES COURAGE

Ava said,
"I *love* these books,
but how can they **help me?**
Who is this *inspiring*
of my **friends** or *family?*"

GARDENER GEORGE
WINS LOCAL
FLOWER SHOW

As she **looked** through **photos** and thought of those she knew, she realized with **amazement** that they were *heroes* too!

The next day,
Ava woke and thought,
"Was all of that for real?"
Her mind buzzed
with excitement and
new ways to think and feel.

She rushed downstairs
and shouted,

"**DAD!**

I have a
*new idea.*

Let's **plant** *flowers* in a box
to **spread** a little *cheer.*"

22

Ava knew that she could do
**much more** to make things **right.**
If her *neighbors* shared their **talents,**
they could make the **streets** look *bright.*

She **wrote** to all her **neighbors**
and told them of her *plan*:

"Let's all work together
and **improve things**

if we can!"

Everybody got involved –

they knew the place looked bad.

They painted and they planted

and they used the skills they had.

Slowly, *life* and **color** spread;
the sun made **flowers** grow;
and people going past
began to **smile** and say *hello*.

DREAM**VIDS**

DREAM TV

-03

Soon, the *story* made the news,
and *Ava* shared her **dream**

of helping people **everywhere**

to spread *joy* as a **team.**

WeDream.

**AVA'S AMAZING STORY**
#inspiring #dreambig
#rainbowpark #community

DREAM
MAGAZINE

*Dreamshare*

**ANYTHING IS POSSIBLE**
#worktogether #spreadjoy
#believeinyourself

Thanks to *Ava* dreaming **big**, she'd **changed** her neighborhood.

Now she **knew** that *life* was full of chances to **do good.**

So Ava learned this lesson:

# Dream Big
and be brave.

Even the **smallest ripple**
can become the *biggest wave.*